ODE TO NUMBERS

ODE TO NUMBERS

Poems by

Sarah Glaz

Antrim House
Simsbury, Connecticut

Library of Congress Control Number: 2017953485

ISBN: 978-1-943826-40-7

First Edition, 2017

Printed & bound by Ingram Spark, LLC

Book design by Rennie McQuilkin

Front cover: "Small Yellow" ("Kleines Gelb")
Wassily Kandinsky, 1926 (oil on composition board)
courtesy of Yale University Art Gallery
gift of Collection Société Anonyme

Author photograph by Shannon McAvoy

Antrim House
860.217.0023
AntrimHouse@comcast.net
www.AntrimHouseBooks.com
21 Goodrich Road, Simsbury, CT 06070

In memory of my parents

TABLE OF CONTENTS

III. SERENDIPITY

IV. LATE AFTERNOON AT THE WORKSHOP ON COMMUTATIVE RINGS

V. EUCLID'S 5TH POSTULATE

Oh, the thirst to know
how many!
The hunger
to know
how many
stars in the sky!

from "Ode to Numbers"
by Pablo Neruda

ODE TO NUMBERS

I. CLOSE TO THE ORIGIN

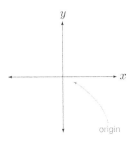

The term "origin" refers to the point of intersection of the coordinate axes. In two dimensions, the origin, denoted by O, is the point with coordinates (0, 0)—the intersection point of the x and y axes.

Close to the Origin

The day stretches its lazy golden arms
       interminably long and elegant
           like x and y axes.

A band of gold glows in the sunshine
       at the center.

It is a symbol of the bond,
       the union of the positive and negative,
       the source from which everything springs.

Along two golden lines
       fingers trace back the time
           before knowing its name

when naming things took time.

    And
           I can almost reach that stretch
              of time without an end in sight,

the union of the positive and negative,
the source from which everything sprang

              out on the infinite plane.

Animals One to Seven

Strada Tudor Vladimirescu 50
Judeţul Călăraşi, Bucureşti

The window opens to a garden.
I could jump out and in, but
I am not allowed. Close to a tree trunk
lilies-of-the-valley drop their
snowy tears. An ant convoy
trails a thin thread of dark.

In spring, we hunt for colored
Easter eggs in newly grown grass.
Snails, after rain, race on the
wooden bench. We sing to lure
them out of their spiral shells:
Melc, melc, codobelc!

Summer simmers through fence
slats where insect-gobbling turkeys
clack their tongues at us.
We tease them back, mercilessly.
Faces as red as fists, throats
swollen up in angst.

A litter of stray kittens hides behind a
bush, five mewling furballs with
closed eyes. One sports a white star
on its forehead like a badge.
My Prince! My Warrior! My Knight!
I want to keep you, but I am not allowed.

Before each Christmas, the fattened pig
in our neighbor's yard squeals: *Murder!*
Murder! I cannot help you curly-tail,
I am too small. And later, baby predator,
through tears and mucus I agree
to take a bite of savory cured ham.

My chicken, grown plump and shiny,
I fear the time is near. Time, endless
when I give permission, runs short when
it arrives. Mother of sins still unforgiven:
you fail to mention time's old
trick before it is too late.

Winter comes bitter cold and icy,
sleigh over rock-hard snow. Stories
beside the fire, window closed. Yet,
through the cracks I feel the breath
of flowers, bouquet of frosted glass.
It will not wilt.

The Europe of My Childhood

Only a poem can invoke
the Europe of my childhood—
words long ago strayed from the path
and found themselves lost
like children in the forest.

And now the classroom where I raised my hand,
excelled in mathematics,
wallows in smells of pencil shavings and wet socks.
Still fills its chairs with those who do not wish to learn
and those who cannot learn,
the one I helped,
the few I failed.
What has become of them?
What does the future hold
if they gave up?
How did they hide
those who could not comply?

So many questions left unanswered
since I went away.

Put words into a hat,
wave a hand above it,
pull out knot by knot
a link of colorful silks,
then a dove flapping its wings
and a rabbit with twitching whiskers
and long ears.

Then the black hole . . .

Trains

You have a train inside you;
a coal-driven engine puffs
black clouds of smoke through your ears;
a deep throated whistle
blows nightly warnings
when you pretend to sleep.
Where will it take you
chugging along as if there is no tomorrow?
Large wheels whir, iron spokes
clang-strike sparks
on steel tracks in your brain.
You are too short to reach
the first carriage doorstep,
short enough to see
the gap underneath it
open into pitch-black darkness,
black ripples of tension
stream dark on dark.
They cry, telling you
We'll miss you!
You try to respond,
thinking of nothing,
blank — the way you always turn
inevitable to adventure,
afloat on smoke drifts toward nowhere.
Your parents fuss over luggage.
Back to back
in the narrow compartment,
they ruffle each other's feathers
at every move.

You press your face to the window pane,
looking out.
Already you cannot distinguish
sharp contours—
dim figures grow dimmer.
Is it a red handkerchief waving,
a pale hand aglow
amidst sooty detail like moon-flesh?
Your breath on the window pane
draws geometric patterns.
This is how it begins.
You correct their shape
with one finger: star,
octagon, circle, flat helix.
Wipe the glass clean
with the dirty heel of your palm
and start again
from scratch.

Do You Believe in Fairytales?

You can
spin a dragon
by its tail,
be caught
in the whirlwind
and propelled
into orbit.
After circling
the earth for
thirteen hundred years
you land
on a moon
that was never
inhabited, but which functions
according to all
the laws of mathematics.
This is the land
of new beginnings:
red sky,
pale purple sun,
magenta clouds
pouring heavy rains
on dense,
primordial vegetation.
Blue creature—you.
I forgot
to mention
that orbiting
the earth is
supposed
to purify the
soul of pain.

Love Story

"If I ever write about you,"
he said,
"it will be a love story,
a story about
how much you want to be loved."

Father, do you love
your little girl?
I brought you
a soup full
of numbers,
formulas chopped to perfection,
integrals fried to a crisp.

Father, is it algebra
you wish
for supper,
or higher mathematics?

I lie at your feet
looking up
at your busy mouth,
waiting for a smile to appear,
a few words of approval and praise,
one word of love.

How long can one wait?

A lifetime if necessary.

Even beyond . . .

Thirteen

There is always happiness at the end of *if,*
just around the corner from the here and now
at the intersection of two dreams.

I strain toward it on nights I cannot sleep.

Climbing the staircase on the thirteenth floor
I dream each step a wooden board   a boat   a crocodile
a stretched fabric of sky with sparklers sewn on it

and on the thirteenth step I find it waiting.

It is open and closed,
wide-eyed and eyes tightly shut,
the past and the future rolled into one—

and I will name it mine.

II. PYTHAGORAS PLAYS HIS LYRE

There is geometry in the humming of the strings, there is music in the spacing of the spheres.

Pythagoras (560 BC–480 BC),
quoted by Aristotle in *Metaphysics*

Pythagoras Plays his Lyre

What is the wisest thing? Number.
What is the most beautiful? Harmony.
        Iamblichus (3rd century AD),
        On the Pythagorean Way of Life

Pythagoras plays his lyre
surrounded by mathematicians.
We sing paeans as he strikes
the cords:

> *We discovered the*
> *law of the cosmos:*
> *All is number!*
> *Mysterious proportions!*
> *The way strings vibrate*
> *to harmonic ratios*
> *makes music sound*
> *like heaven.*
> *The sacred beans sprout*
> *in the nearby fields.*
> *All animals are part*
> *of our family.*
> *In the interval between*
> *earth and the firmament*
> *planets circle and hum*
> *in concert.*
> *Each One a note*
> *in the grand symphony*
> *of all creation.*
> *We guard*
> *its innermost secret.*

The music wafts upward
like smoke from burnt incense
pleasing the gods who watch us
play and pass.

$$\sqrt{2} = 1.41421\ldots\ldots$$

We started our voyage on the gulf of Tarentum.

The sea was choppy
and the brothers were restless.
At dawn, we gathered on the deck
intent to solve the conflict like rational men.

Hippasus still refused to keep the secret.

He had discovered that
the diagonal of a square
is incommensurable
with its side.

Alas! Our world had collapsed
and so did our geometric proofs.

Too much to lose, we heaved him overboard.

The First Negative

Down the funnel of history
I search for you—the first man
to cup in his hands
minus one grain of fire:

"*Ghost of departed quantity!*
Mysterious absence!
I am afraid
I am cradling an illusion!"

Yet from my vantage point
I discern a sign
upon the still uncharted number line
where negatives

began to light the way
for abstract algebra to come into existence
several thousand years
in the future.

Numbers and Letters

The symbols of Mnemosyne
don't get along.
Today I heard a quarrel between B and 2,
and even as we speak, this lazy eight ∞
shamelessly stretched without a limit on a limb,
pushes numbers and letters towards the outer edge.
From a to z or 0 to ∞ —
a single source does not suffice
for peaceful coexistence.
They once were born-together twins,
offspring of mother memory and father wealth,
both trained from infancy as record keepers
of the first thousand kegs of wine and beer
produced by the first thousand settlers around Ur
who, tired of forever shearing wool,
started a very lucrative and joyful business:
planting of hops, barley, and grapes,
fermenting juices,
and who, in their spare time,
sloshed and satisfied,
took to the flute and lute
and sang long hymns of thanks,
recited endless stories of nomadic pasts,
composed numerous tunes of praise:
Praised be Marduk,
Nisaba shall be praised,
revered the moon god Nana,
and powerful Inana.
And to ensure

they left tradition for the children,
in brewing, counting, and song alike,
imprinted symbols
with sharp-angled wedges
into the region's malleable clay
and baked them in hot kilns.
In the beginning, letters and numbers
looked alike, happily shared a tablet . . .

The Death of Euclid

So great was Euclid's fame that he was known to the Greeks as ὁ στοιχειωτής, "teacher of the Elements."
D. E. Smith, *History of Mathematics*

And onto the barge decked with flowers
we lifted him   our arms dark and
strong   his body shrunk in its
shroud of warm roses   The Nile's
sluggish brown flow   Myth floating
in front of us like the cloud of God
We lifted his eyes towards heaven
where he saw the next generation
inherit   and we mourned   how
we mourned his fine-tuned mind
his irreplaceable jewels of thought   Not
one of us came close   in our search
for truth   to match his erudition
Not one of us came close   And
the barge groaned under his almost
weightless body   once   as if in pain
then clutched his mutilated heart
to its own   Crocodiles circled silently
plucking at wilted flowers   And the
procession started slowly   heavy
with sighs   ghost deep   oars into
water and heaving   mud splashing
dipping and cutting a path   upstream
we left on the shore   rooted   tangled
in tears   our imaginations seeking
relief in words of reverence

$12=2^2\text{x}3$ Anuk is dying for Anuk is dying in the white of winter
11   The coldest month
$10=2\text{x}5$ Anuk is dying in the falling snow
$9=3^2$ The white of winter for Anuk is dying
$8=2^3$ Anuk is dying for the white of winter
7   The drift of time
$6=2\text{x}3$ Anuk is dying in the white of winter
5   The falling snow
$4=2^2$ Anuk is dying for Anuk is dying
3   The white of winter
2   Anuk is dying
1   .

I Am a Number

1

I am tall
and
one sided
like an ostrich
Pluck
the eye
of my feather
Whittle
the stick
of
remembrance
bare
of
ornamentation
I am alone

2

I am fat with contentment
In the arc
of survival
we win
by a hair
Kick
the less
fortunate
down the plank
to make space

3

I am prime
and conflicted
One more or one less
The spoke in the wheel
or grease that makes it go
Increase and multiply
or divide
and divorce

4

I am Parmenides' *many*
on the edge of ancient counting:
the stars in the sky
fattened sheep of pharaoh
the dappled cows of the gods grazing under the sun
and all the grains of sand
on the seashore

I Am a Number II

5

Forged in time's fire
my golden figure
rises
open
to the past
and the future
I count my digits
All present
yet only
half way there

6

I can be factored
into selves
from
former lives
each one
more potent
than
I
am
Unmultiplied
I disappear

7

Last prime
before
the count of years
halts
and
the great mystery
begins

8

How did it come to that

9

I have no time

10

Decem

Calculus

I tell my students the story of Newton versus Leibniz,
the war of symbols, lasting five generations,
between The Continent and British Isles,
involving deeply hurt sensibilities
and grievous blows to national pride
on such weighty issues as publication priority
and working systems of logical notation:
whether the derivative must be denoted by a "prime,"
an apostrophe atop the right-hand corner of a function,
evaluated by Newton's fluxions method $\Delta y/\Delta x$;
or by a formal quotient of differentials dy/dx,
intimating future possibilities,
terminology that guides the mind.
The genius of both men lies in grasping simplicity
out of the swirl of ideas guarded by Chaos,
becoming channels through which her light poured clarity
on the relation binding slope of tangent line
to area of planar region lying below a curve.
The Fundamental Theorem of Calculus,
basis of modern mathematics, claims nothing more.

While Leibniz—suave, debonair, philosopher and politician,
published his proof to jubilant cheers of continental followers,
the Isles seethed, unnerved.
They knew of Newton's secret files,
locked in deep secret drawers—
for fear of theft and from stranger paranoid delusions,
hiding an earlier version of the same result.
The battle escalated to public accusations,
charges of blatant plagiarism,

excommunication from The Royal Math. Society,
a few blackened eyes,
(no duels),
and raged long after both men were buried,
splitting Isles from Continent, barring unified progress,
till black bile drained and turbulent spirits becalmed.

Calculus—Latin for small stones,
primitive means of calculation; evolving to abaci;
later to principles of enumeration advanced by widespread use
of the Hindu-Arabic numeral system employed to this day,
as practiced by *algebristas*—barbers and bone setters in Medieval Spain;
before Calculus came the Σ (*sigma*) notion—
sums of infinite yet countable series;
and culminating in addition of uncountable many dimensionless
    line segments—
the integral $\int$—snake,
first to thirst for knowledge, at any price.

That abstract concepts, applicable in the beginning
merely to unseen, unsensed objects—orbits of distant stars—
could generate intense earthly passion
is inconceivable today,
when Mathematics is considered a dry discipline,
depleted of life sap, devoid of emotion,
alive only in convoluted brain cells of weird scientific minds.

The Enigmatic Number *e*

It ambushed Napier at Gartness,
like a swashbuckling pirate
leaping from the base.
He felt its power, but never realized its nature.
e's first appearance in disguise—a tabular array
of values of *ln*, was logged in an appendix
to Napier's posthumous publication.
Oughtred, inventor of the circular slide rule,
still ignorant of *e*'s true role,
performed the calculations.

A hundred thirteen years the hit and run went on.
There and not there—elusive *e*,
escape artist and trickster,
wove in and out of minds and computations:
Saint-Vincent caught a glimpse of it under rectangular hyperbolas;
Huygens mistook its rising trace for logarithmic curve;
Nicolaus Mercator described its *log* as natural
without accounting for its base;
Jacob Bernoulli, compounding interest continuously,
came close, yet failed to recognize its face;
and Leibniz grasped it hiding in the maze of calculus,
natural basis for comprehending change—but
misidentified as *b*.

The name was first recorded in a letter
Euler sent Goldbach in November 1731:
"e denotat hic numerum, cujus logarithmus hyperbolicus est = 1."
Since *a* was taken, and Euler
was partial to vowels,

e rushed to make a claim—the next in line.

We sometimes call *e* Euler's Number: he knew
e in its infancy as *2.718281828459045235.*

On Wednesday, 6th of May, 2009,
e revealed itself to Kondo and Pagliarulo,
digit by digit, to *200,000,000,000* decimal places.
It found a new digital game to play.

In retrospect, following Euler's naming,
e lifted its black mask and showed its limit:

$$e = \lim_{n \to \infty} \left(1 + \frac{1}{n}\right)^n$$

Bernoulli's compounded interest for an investment of one.

Its reciprocal gave Bernoulli many trials,
from gambling at the slot machines to deranged parties
where nameless gentlemen checked hats with butlers at the door,
and when they left, *e*'s reciprocal handed each a stranger's hat.

In gratitude to Euler, *e* showed a serious side,
infinite sum representation:

$$e = \sum_{n=0}^{\infty} \frac{1}{n!} = \frac{1}{0!} + \frac{1}{1!} + \frac{1}{2!} + \frac{1}{3!} + \cdots$$

For Euler's eyes alone, *e* fanned the peacock tail of
(e - 1)/2 's continued fraction expansion,
displaying patterns that confirmed
its own irrationality.

A century passed till *e*—through Hermite's pen—
was proved to be a transcendental number.

But to this day it teases us with
speculations about e^{e}.

e's abstract beauty casts a glow on Euler's Identity:

$$e^{i\pi} + 1 = 0$$

the elegant, mysterious equation,
where waltzing arm in arm with i and π,
e flirts with complex numbers and roots of unity.

We meet e nowadays in functional high places
of Calculus, Differential Equations, Probability, Number Theory,
and other ancient realms:

$$y = e^{x}$$

e is the base of the unique exponential function
whose derivative is equal to itself.
The more things change the more they stay the same.

e gathers gravitas as solid under integration,

$$\int e^{x} dx = e^{x} + c$$

a constant c, is the mere difference.
And often e makes guest appearances in Taylor series expansions.
And now and then e stars in published poetry—
honors and administrative duties multiply with age.

If Not Loved, Then Useful

Facing my students'
sighs and questions,
I realize they do not love
the abstract symbols
whose patterns shape my life.

For them the daring mystery
of algebraic equations
and the elusive charm of geometric figures
are equally incongruous as objects of
great love and admiration.

If not loved, then useful—

and for you, my dears,
I try to illustrate the miracle
by which the laws of nature
glimpsed through formulas
devised by human mind
(although, I must admit, but poor approximations)
acquire comprehensible dimensions
which may predict the future
or illuminate the past:

where hurricanes will hit the shore
and with what force,
the weight of passing cars across a bridge
that won't collapse,
the purity of water
flowing from your faucet,
the quality of air you breathe.

Mysteries

This summer I am connected to reality by an umbilical cord.
Who knows how long before I can escape into imagination:
my mathematics, pure abstraction—groups, modules, rings
(coherent and other finite-conductor conditions). Yet, I read
Mathematical Modeling in the Environment for the sake of
my students, who seem to possess a more practical streak.
The book describes the construction of various mathematical
models involved in the study of ground water and air pollution
and in hazardous material management. I read and I am struck
anew by the uncanny fit between the language of mathematics—
pure product of human invention, clever mind-game comparable
to chess—and the intricate workings of the natural world, a
model of such descriptive power as to be able to predict with
a high degree of accuracy future, apparently random, natural
events. And I believe that we are meant to understand the
mysteries, but slowly, every few billion years a revelation,
till the convergence point is reached when everything opens
and closes, and when humanity becomes brains, becomes
knowledge, and the planet empties of flesh.

Mathematical Modeling

Mathematical modeling may be viewed
As an organizing principle
That enables us to handle
A vast array of information

As an organizing principle
We could use the color spectrum
A vast array of information
Would become a rainbow in the sky

We could use the color spectrum
And the scaling notes spanning an octave
Would become a rainbow in the sky
Shining through the melody of rain

And the scaling notes spanning an octave
And letters gleaned from ancient alphabets
Shining through the melody of rain
Nature translated into words

And letters gleaned from ancient alphabets
That enable us to handle
Nature translated into words
May be viewed as mathematical modeling

Eclipse, a Love Poem

The moon writes a letter on sun's face: an inverted C
looking backwards toward a point of no return.

Later, a perfect O appears: O as in *l*O*ve,*
a love letter—the moon emerges from a cloud at

the precise center of the blaze, blinding the naked
eye. Then the slow withdrawal begins: C reverts to

normal position— light seeking a mirror image
of itself. How different things might have been given

another angle:∪—the *union* sign mysteriously
formed in the penumbra, or upside-down ∩—symbol

for *intersection* culled from the alphabet of mathematics. Imagination's play on closeness at a distance.

Sun Plus Moon by Karl Kempton

A Pantoum for the Power of Theorems

The power of the Invertible Matrix Theorem
lies in the connections it provides among so
many important concepts . . . It should be
emphasized, however, that the Invertible Matrix
Theorem applies only to square matrices.

> David C. Lay,
> *Linear Algebra and Its Applications*

The power of a theorem lies
In the connections it provides
Among many important concepts
Under a certain set of assumptions.

In the connections it provides
We are always able to find
Under a certain set of assumptions
Some that fell through the cracks.

We are always able to find
Neglected aspects of ourselves
Some that fell through the cracks
Left unexplored by mathematics.

Neglected aspects of ourselves
(The power of a theorem lies)
Left unexplored by mathematics
Among many important concepts.

What Can We Do If We Crave Certainty in Mathematics?

Thus, to salvage traditional mathematics, Hilbert proposed a bold new program. It required first that the whole of existing mathematics should be axiomatized, and second that this axiomatic theory should then be proven consistent.

David M. Burton, *The History of Mathematics*

Hilbert said, "No one shall expel us from
the paradise that Cantor has created." And we believed,
like Cantor himself, that God had opened the gates
to the forbidden garden,
had invited us to enter,
meet ℵ (*aleph*) face to face,
converse in the language of sets,
admire the ascent of transfinite cardinals
into an infinitude of infinities.
No one can possess such knowledge and remain unscathed.
We lost our footing; doubts assaulted us
from the very first step,
set roadblocks in our path—
unanswerable questions, inexplicable paradoxes
and baffling results.

Before Kurt Gödel, we could still have hoped.
Attempting to resolve inconsistencies,
we could have spent our lives trying to grasp the tantalizing
cloud of certainty hanging above our heads—
just beyond reach.

The naïveté of Frege, Russell, Hilbert,
and all of us, their followers,

divided into schools with bombastic titles—
Axiomatic, Logistic, Formalistic—
with methods and approaches,
plans for the future,
a list of problems to last to the end of time.
Little did we know of logic's limitations:
that our system would backfire,
stating its own incompleteness,
in its own ink signing the QED—
that with cymbals and umlauts
it would prove its inability to prove
consistency of axioms within the system.
And what else was there but the system
we took for granted
as we did our ability to breathe?

After Gödel proved the Incompleteness Theorems
a grey cloud descended upon us—
we could touch the fog.
Nothing was pure logic.
Pure logic was nothing.
We could not even count on knowing what truth
can be proved.
Uncertainty permeated everything.

We prayed that this was not the end of the road—
that there was more of it to travel.

Hardy

It is a melancholy experience for a professional mathematician to find himself writing about mathematics.

G.H. Hardy, *A Mathematician's Apology*

It used to be mathematics once
I visited to drink a cup of peace;
I climbed the ladder rung by rung,
reaching the highest platform.
It used to be mathematics once
I went to meet.
I left the world behind in search of peace of mind;
I flew out of myself on a trajectory of hope.
It used to be mathematics once,
clear unadulterated thought,
for which I yearned.
Among the stars it led.
I followed unafraid.
No fall, no bread, no tears,
not even cries of joy allowed—
untouched pure beauty
my mind alone perceived
and brought it out
of its invisibility into the light.
It used to be mathematics once—
both quest and goal—
the only place of rest my mind had known.

III. SERENDIPITY

Rings are abstract algebraic structures in which two operations are defined—called (by analogy) addition and multiplication—that have similar properties to the addition and multiplication defined for numbers. A commutative ring is a ring in which the multiplication operation is commutative. The study of commutative rings is called Commutative Ring Theory.

Serendipity

I work on mathematics
the way I work on poems—
that's why
I work alone.
For how illumination comes
and where it comes from
is a mystery.
It is as if
I am an empty vessel—
filled only
with intent—
prepared and waiting
for the flow of light.
A certain proof
or proper words
expressing a truth
could find me
no other way.

A Woman in Love

A woman in love sees
a trace of her beloved
in every man she meets:
a gesture or a glance,
a single strand of hair,
the shadow of a smile.
I see a streak of mathematics
in almost everything.

A New Research Project

A new research project like a newborn baby
surprises you with the amount of work it asks
for. At every step ten times or more than
you imagined and a few steps above the ones
you counted on. And yet it is effortless action.
Who counts uninterrupted joy as burden,
a flow which gently sweeps you off your feet
into the magic world of expectations? Immersed
in love for the precious fruit of your labor,
miraculous involvement in creation at your age,
you thank God for the gift of fertility altered—
I will not laugh behind my hand in disrespect—
and carry on with your design.

Commutative Coherent Rings

It took five years to write the book
which made me a mathematician—
an expert in coherent rings.
I bow in gratitude for the magnanimous gift:
that You bestowed on me the
knowledge of Your secrets and let me
play for You the music of the spheres.
Your own notes endowed me with
thoughts of the great questions still
unsolved and let me answer some in
human tongue. And when I fumbled
in the dark, all lights extinguished,
You let me rummage through the
manuscripts of time for a new radiance
to save my life: Hilbert Polynomials,
the golden thread woven into the
algebraic fabric of the universe,
luminous with multiplicity.

The Journey

I can best describe my experience of doing mathematics in terms of a journey...

> Andrew Wiles, on the occasion of solving the 300-years-old conjecture called "Fermat's Last Theorem" (PBS NOVA program, *The Proof,* 1994)

You wait till the unconscious makes the unknown known—
till you embark on the right journey
and start to walk the correct path,
twisting among tall trees and tangled bushes,
the path which finally arrives.
Once there, the clearing seems at first a jewel,
small and vivid, an emerald winking seductively mid forest-green.
On close inspection, it is the sparkling green of water—
it's water for the grasses, it's nourishment for the wild flowers.
And soon the ground appears dappled with their magic colors:
blue is for lemmas, orange for corollaries,
red is for propositions, pink for remarks,
and purples—saved for theorems—crisscross the field.
The clearing grows into a wide expanse,
the trees recede to the periphery, and in the distance—
majestic and somewhat sinister—
they sway and murmur of dark secrets.
They stand around the open land in a protective circle,
the sentinels which clearly show you there are borders,
a limit to your understanding and power of deduction.
And silently, when you acknowledge
you have exhausted all present resources,
know each blade of grass and every bloom
as intimately as you know your lover's skin,
they lure you with the promise of a quest—
to venture forth into dense shadows once again.

Like a Mathematical Proof

A poem courses through me
like a mathematical proof,
arriving whole from nowhere,
from a distant galaxy of thought.
It pours on paper
impatiently
faster than my hand
can write,
stretches wings,
flaps,
twists and turns,
strikes sparks as it forms.
It is a creature
of indescribable
mystery
like a mathematical proof—
its passage
fills me
with
inner peace.

Window to Venice by Ron Glaz

In My Study

Perhaps I should not take
so much delight in objects:
the way a green light filters
through the window screen
casting a light-green glow on glass
under the twenty-inch
wide screen of my computer.
Perhaps I should instead
sit in the chair and do my work.
The wall behind the desk,
on its right-hand side,
is blank and asking
for Ronnie's photographs
of Venice to display
the rosy shades of buildings
reflected in the water down below,
the elegantly arching bow
of a dilapidated boat
tied to a post,
a green background all around
enhanced by the distressed green
paint of wooden frame.
All this I see in my mind's eye
and know tomorrow it will be there
above the printer and the fax machine.
And underneath bare feet
the soft and yielding whisper
of the hand-knotted oriental rug
teases my toes.
No work today? No work.

I Climbed the Himalayas

I
climbed
the Himalayas.
On my way to the top—
between elevations 29,000 and 29, 001—
my foot slipped on a rock,
made an ungraceful skip.
Oh! Obligation to perfection
unfulfilled.

Not Human

When the young woman said "Not human,"
I wondered what would I do under those circumstances.
    I would cringe and withdraw,
    never to venture into that place again,
    keep my photographic memory from prying eyes,
    my love of numbers—the calm descending
    over me as I inhabit their language—a secret from the world,
    even the shapes and colors of my childhood dreams—before
    the god of monochrome washed them away—unshared.
What did Daniel do?
The opposite.

Mathematical Models of Rejection

He expands on the theory of DNA splitting,
complex computations designed to predict
complete strings of genes,
humanity reduced to a common denominator,
stripped down to essentials,
displayed for inspection on monitor screens.
A fantastical opportunity for a mathematician:
crunch numbers in the service of real
life perplexities,
lend a hand of precision to model
the inaccurate world.
I admire his ability to bounce back from rejection,
a few gray strands dimming the red curls,
several pounds lost
around his belt,
a slight tremor twitching his eyelid
betraying emotions,
yet the glint behind them clear:
I will show the bastards
on their own terms!
I wonder if one can measure the minute difference,
construct a scientific model
for weight-bearing capacity
that keeps one afloat
on currents of anger
and lets another sink to the bottom
in an ocean of words.

Man Among Men

With the ground beasts
matching tusk to tusk
in the clearing, I think
Father—this is not for me—
fight your own battles—
I cannot become the son
you never had
and always wanted.
And the tusks penetrate
the skin, the skin
slides its sheath of blood—
raw flesh against raw flesh.
Only the resilient
survives.
On the porch they swill
beer and malign colleagues—
Ah . . . the good life—the world
as it is meant to be.
You gore and tear to shreds
another's innards;
he does the same to you.
May the best man win!
Then comes
     grudging respect
     and constant vigilance—
The world as it is meant to be—
     Friends!

Eventually It Arrives

Eventually it arrives
        late   maybe too late
        when the air is heavy with whispers
        of spring in the branches.

Eventually after fights
        after an interminable wait
        after giving up
        it arrives in a strange form
        almost unacceptable.

I knew not to count on you
        to hand me my right
        as a gift with no
        price tag attached.

I knew   but in my heart
        hope struggled with
        knowledge
        and won.

Your sons are climbing the slope
        to the top
        wearing your shoes
        equipped from your storage
        with strong climbing gear.

Your daughter hand-over-hand
        claws her way up the hill
        through thorny bramble

and jagged rock
slow and alone
unaided by you.

Her backpack holds theorems.
That is how it is.

No End in Sight

Four lines a day, no more—no less.
Learn to live with restrictions
and constrictions, dense within
the nowhere space.

No Matter What I Do

My garden is neglected;
I grow poems instead.
Sometimes I wonder if,
between aptitude
and financial need,
I took a wrong turn,
arrived at weeds.
Occasional forsythias bloom
on bushes sprouted
out of windblown seeds
from other people's gardens,
and tiger lilies'
freckled orange faces
show up every spring
no matter what I do.
Garden of unplanned blooms,
not many thanks to me.
I grew equations instead,
abstract rings,
before the drought
spread words
on top of cracked earth
and poems sprouted.
Somewhere along the way,
I took a wrong turn,
and found confusion.
Confusion.
Confusion,
no matter what I do.

The Integers Are Not a Happy Medium

When I arrive
he is already there,
waiting.
A shadow swiftly fleets across his brow.
"The integers are not a happy medium,"
he says by way of greeting.
"They fly which way,
scatter without restraint,
fritter through fingers faster
than one can count the gains,
and you are late again."
Perhaps I hear this only in my head.

Late Arrival

I arrive late to everything—
twenty years between station and station:

The train lost its axle,
The tracks derailed the engine.

Excuses, excuses...

Straining my neck, I see
through dusty panes of glass
the faded hieroglyphics of ambition
lighting a patch of sky.

I could have walked much faster
but I love the ride,
its glamour of decay and sadness,
a crown of spider-webs
around a corner of neglected time.

I imagine myself discovered
a hundred years into the future.
My late train arrives
and I step down on tomorrow's platform
without any fanfare.

IV. LATE AFTERNOON AT THE WORKSHOP ON COMMUTATIVE RINGS

Life is an unfoldment, and the further we travel the more truth we can comprehend.

Hypatia (370 AD–415 AD), quoted by Elbert Hubbard in *Little Journeys to the Homes of Great Teachers*

Late Afternoon at the Workshop
on Commutative Rings

Il Palazzone, Cortona, Italy, June 2006

Day One

Window wide open,
shutters pushed aside,
Tuscan hills in morning light—
a herd of sheared fat sheep.

Day Two

Early afternoon out of blue sky
a barrage of hail the size of pheasant eggs.
The inner courtyard instantly fills.
A small dog is frantic, scampers and barks.
Five minutes later—as if it never was.

Day Three

"The nature of a faithful content ideal
of a Gaussian polynomial over a commutative ring"
(a source of excitement for a number of years)
"proves to be locally principal."

The first idea relayed from mind to mind
at last reached perfect formulation.

Days Four to Seven

Vino rosso   O   Vino rosso
silken on the palate like a Puccini aria
on the lips of Maria Callas.

Inebriated in Pienza and Montepulciano
Cortona   Firenze   and   San Gimignano

Brindisi! Salute! Chin-chin!

To our quest!

Trieste, 1994: Celebration

The Hotel Mignon in Trieste,
Grignano, Miramare
(to keep tabs on reality
I record every beat of life)
is owned by la patrona.
I do not know her name—
perhaps Anna-Maria,
Claudia, Sofia.
Those names seem to suit
her simple confidence,
airy Tiramisu
drenched in brandy (Amaretto?),
the bira piccola,
grilled calamari
and insalata mista.
Her husband is Marco,
or Angelo, or Mario.
He loves to eat pasta,
it shows on his figure.
He piles empty kegs
of beer behind the albergo.
He may be the one
who changes the towels,
and makes up my bed
with an extra blanket.
Friday, he drives me
to the airport
at the crack of dawn
for thirty thousand lire.
Today it rains in Grignano,

the outskirts of Trieste.
On Via Junker
steps run up and down,
leading to
the Continua
and the Adriatic Sea
(respectively).
Tomorrow morning
I take an early train
to Venezia.
The fishermen come home
loaded with catch;
they sing an aria
I cannot quite place—
boat to shore level,
ropes to pier posts,
a wonderful duet.
I have dinner alone
at the trattoria,
when out of nowhere
it arrives—
the long-awaited
argument
that clinches the proof.

Ghazal: Resonant Air

Suddenly summer rain dances through fragrant air,
leaps on leaf trampolines, somersaults in buoyant air.

Turtle doves take refuge, gurgling cues, under eaves,
coo-coey-coo, coo-coey-coo, flutter and flit—migrant air.

Once Farinelli sang *Ombra mai fu* at La Fenice, Venezia,
a voice without a shadow casting a spell—radiant air.

All afternoon my love and I sip wine and eavesdrop on
the waves, *love-and-leave, love-and-leave*—undulant air.

Unmoored, a gondola glides by the *Acqua Alta* flooded
street. Wanderers' serendipity—kiss of flamboyant air.

Faraway galaxies lure with a promise of life. God of
trees, seas, beauty, and birds: Grant us water! Grant air!

Perpendicular lines delineate a grid on the map. Three-
quarters stone dead, but in the last quadrant—air.

Don't say *Let us eat and drink for tomorrow we die;*
prepare bread and wine, song and dance—tolerant air.

The desert breathes deep at sunrise, before the sands spin
fire and the heat ripples beneath a dome of flagrant air.

Sarah laughs when she hears the gazelle's dying cry: in
the end it resembles the sound of her song—resonant air.

Marseille, 1997: Night Music

June twenty-first.
Night music spills out of the streets of Paris
south and through the streets of Marseille
along the quay
light inundates the water.
A moon-twin swings back and forth
under the prow of a white ship.
By two a.m.
the crowd thins.
I flow with it
from group to group;
the music follows me.
A Frenchman plucks
the strings of his guitar,
chanting a sad chanson.
His eyes invite me—
S'il vous plait
join the melody and song,
join the red-nosed wino who bums a cigarette,
whose tattered pantleg quivers, keeping time,
join the tall black woman without a brassiere
who sways and croons and blows him
kisses each time
he seems to strike
a special note.
Across the wide boulevard
rhythmic tam-tam—African drums
to which the night faintly vibrates.
Megaphones hanging above marble doorways
croak American rock

and German lieders rattle around corners
while choral sacred songs roll oiled o's
out of mouths of chaste nuns.
Notre Dame de la Garde
upon her mountain pedestal
watches her city swing.
I also cannot sleep or work on mathematics
and back at my hotel,
windows wide open
to the night and shadowy gargoyles,
I call to hear your voice.
The disembodied sound
of answering machine
distant and dim
replies.
Everything far away stays far away.

Arles, 1999: Women in Summer Heat

Riva lies ill on an uncomfortable bed
in Maine, cut off from anyone she knows.
She canceled the plane tickets,
her husband far away,
refrigerator empty, cupboard bare.
Friends warned of the impending trip
don't call. She nurses her high fever
with freshly brewed herb tea
and vegetables from her backyard garden.
I do not exist in the world, she writes,
just in myself.

And Leah, long ago, when
we were still on friendly
terms, confessed: *Sometimes
I feel like hopping on a bus,
leaving my life behind.*

This summer in Provence,
I sit at an outdoor café in
Arles, Place du Forum,
sipping sirop de menthe diluted
with cold water.
It is a torrid day.
The tablecloths stretch to the edge
of the shadow a flickering
field of sunflowers.
Van Gogh's green tongue
licks perspiration
off my back. A man

plucks the strings of his guitar,
passing around a hat.
My loves—an immutable ache
across the water. *What if*
I never go back home?

Luminy light

I choose a place
   according to the quality
           of light
despite the old ghosts
standing on the path
blocking the way.

Winding up the hill
   and on the hilltop
       sky
as large as a boat's sail
seen from underneath
in the clear light
      of Provence.

Water wavelets,

    sparkles,

    slivers of mirror,

and the place I choose
bathed in light
   and dappled
      with sunshine
weaves the golden
    ratio
in its angular
proportions.

The shy girl I used to be
   saw
      this light
   long ago
under another sky.

It appears unexpectedly
     from time to time.

But not much.

Departures in May

Big things crush inside the brain
like plaster of Paris on stone,
a taste of splintered metal,
terracotta hardness of heart's desire.
Statues, motionless
at railroad depots,
proclaim imitation as life.
A white bird flies low above platforms,
sweeps over train cars—
its touch arrests all motion in its tracks.
The Orient Express of boundless energy
soundlessly waits for late chances.
It has been to Paris-Roma-Venezia,
witnessed the grid of time
curve in space, fluid,
twined arcs convergent at infinity
defying Euclid.
Suspended on the clear May sky
ominous signs,
grave formulas,
the white droppings of the aged snow bird—
death white.

Bat Yam, 1963: Sirens

Language leaks into language
with a different accent,
a guttural sound of old friends.
Words travel light in translation
across the ocean I laid between us—
fleeing.

It is hot in July,
torrid in August,
in September sweat crusts on eyelids
like turtle shells, distorting vision.

At night I visit again the house of mirrors,
in touch with my younger self,
defying time.

At four in the morning
ping-ping of milk bottles,
warm smells of freshly baked bread,
sweet-scented pink and white oleander,
the Shacharit prayer rising loud and insistent
from open windows of a nearby Synagogue.

Late afternoon
the sky is pierced by sirens.
My father and I ignore the shelter,
eyes searching high for stray planes.
An alert mind can hear the whistle,
the explosion like an unexpected thunder,
triangulate the location where shrapnel flies,
then hush...

On the Way to New Jersey in Winter of 2000

A Fibonacci sequence poem

I

look

out of

the window

of the slow moving

train to catch the unexpected.

At six a.m., the sun is a young child rising out

of bed with an uncertain smile—awake, but still dreaming. Birds
perched on surfaces of

water build mirror cities. Between city and city, an expanse of
white sand. The sand looks cool and light. Cylindrical containers
of

Wyatt Oil Company play hide and seek, in pink. And although
I can model the air pollution they emit using a Gaussian
Plume equation, I can compute the extent of ground water
contamination that may

result from a small breach at a circular tank's base over a given
amount of time, and I can estimate the risk to human health, in

hypothetical (but likely to occur) emergencies employing a HAZMAT modeling package, I find them beautiful beyond belief. All bathed in morning light, scrubbed pink and clean, powdered, disrobed and Rubenesque.

Behind the farthest one hides a tall crane, its long neck and gangling limbs crisscrossed with black steel patterns like lacy lingerie. On the horizon, against a backdrop of urban sky, shadowy boxes of skyscrapers, and close by, a field of wheat or barley nodding fat whiskered heads heavy with sleep and nourishment. I am preparing my ten o'clock lecture on coherent rings. I cast down my eyes to the yellow pad in my lap—moment of inattention taken as offense. The train lets out a shriek, a trumpet screech, a toot, an electronic overture to a triumphal march.

Tallahassee, 2004: Puzzles

At a conference in Tallahassee
(sibilant sounds like two snakes mating)
I depart before arriving.

Out of the window a cold wink of summer.

I walk the twin-weights of my past and my future,
the load of my present
(the reasons for my absence)
and my expanding figure.

I hold tight to my wishes
and loosely to my fears.

If I were not divided
who would I be?

A Postcard from Transmeria

On New Year's Eve
I wrote you a postcard
from Transmeria:
People here are concerned
with estimating
the surface tension
of the moon.

You answered
with elaborate calculations,
the way you always do,
trying to lure me into
collaboration.
But Sarah,
you added as a postscript,
in Transmeria
the moon is closer to
the outer layer of the planet
than here on earth, and
it is easier to be impressed
by relevancy of
irrelevant results.
As for us,
let's turn time back to yesterday
and forgive.

Should I?

Sixty's Blues with Numbers and a Kiss

A kiss on your bald pate, Joe,
my long-time love.
The plane is hurling through the clouds
at 1800 miles per hour.
Outdoors the temperature is minus 20 Fahrenheit and falling.
Remaining time to destination from Paris
to New York is 4 hours and 50 minutes.
I can see you, but I cannot see myself:
inside, I do not feel the motion—
I am the young girl on the banks of the Seine,
my lips gracefully touching
the tip of a baguette.
I gaze upward and on each chimney
a nesting pigeon prepares
the next generation to fly.
Meanwhile, time speeds by relentlessly
faster and faster
towards home.

Prague, 2007: Out of Season

For everything there is a season—

out of season things struggle and do not survive
or turn ridiculous like Millie's mother
who braided her hair with pink ribbons,
wore miniskirts shorter than her daughter's
and lisped a baby talk—
the laughing stock of the entire neighborhood.

Out of season and jet-lagged in Prague
I listen to the foreign sounds beneath my window—
a woman cries or laughs,
the sounds so similar
that for a moment I pause and strain to hear words.
The words are a soft jumble,
a churning of the tongue,
a cheer or a chock.

It is very cold and my clothes belong
to the season at home.

It is bright light when inside I feel night and dark
when the sun ascends behind the trees of my back yard.

And here a bus stop and a subway ride away
from a big jewel of a city
I feel as isolated as the sycamore I see out of my window
raising above dwarf pines, looking disheveled,
its soft leaves hanging downward

brushing the needle tips.
At home the pines tower over the sycamores.

Does the season for travel in search of scholarship and fame
belong to the young?

Fes, 2008: Lovely, Lovely

Early in the morning
The mist rises over the valley
At the rim
Mountains slope in ragged patches
Green alternates with earthy ochre
Lovely the fragrance rising with the mist
A burnt offering of
Incense and spices
The lights of the royal palace
In the distance dimmed by the waking sun
Lovely the buzz of flies
And in the grasses insect-music
Black dogs elegantly pace
Around the compound
Rumors of monkeys and wild boar
Two electrical poles
Slide down the mountain
Strung with high voltage wires
The isolation ...

The smell of sandalwood
Two drops of perfume behind each ear
All day whispering veiled secrets
African worn-out hills
Twisted trees and short grasses
Ski slopes and bald patches
Monkeys
Wild boar
Stray dogs around the compound
Hind legs elegantly kicking backward

Sun-crumbled earth
In universal acknowledgment
Of their species

Three birds swoop low over the valley
Rise and fall
Glide in circles
Follow an ancient pattern
The waking sun turns them black and burnished
Like charcoal butterflies on a background
Of washed-out blue
Drawing the golden grasses upward and out
Orchestrating their motion
Undulating waves on a vast yellow sea

The unveiling of Nouf takes place
Late afternoon
Mantle tossed aside
Black chador rises
And the glimpse dazzles
Red silk gold bangles
A touch of musk and sandalwood
On milk and honey skin
Layers and layers
Of mystery and seduction
Dispensed as parting gifts
Under the mild gaze of her husband
Medjool dates and oil perfumes
To please us western women
Wrinkled
By sun and wind
Free and unchaperoned

At the end all is so lovely
Lovely and strange
Engraved in memory
Tomorrow I leave for Europe
Perhaps I shall never return as
A mathematician at a conference
Perhaps I shall never return

Lisbon, 2011: Full Circle

I bought on a street corner in Lisbon
a mandala made of wire and stones.
It hangs around my neck on a black velvet cord
and glimmers in sunshine carnelian red.

A mandala made of wire and stones
it flexes to become a rhomboid or sphere
and glimmers in sunshine carnelian red
color of inner self that matches my skin.

It flexes to become a rhomboid or sphere
wheel of life transformed by sacred geometry,
color of inner self that matches my skin.
Even a scientist believes in omens and signs.

Wheel of life transformed by sacred geometry
I bought on a street corner in Lisbon.
Even a scientist believes in omens and signs.
It hangs around my neck on a black velvet cord.

V. EUCLID'S 5TH POSTULATE

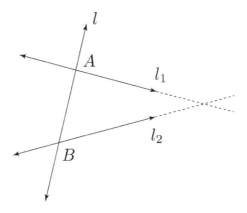

That, if a straight line falling on two straight lines makes the interior angles on the same side less than two right angles, the two straight lines, if produced indefinitely, meet on that side on which the angles are less than the two right angles.

Euclid (325 BC–265 BC), *The Elements*, Book I, Postulate 5
(also called "Euclid's Parallel Postulate")

Euclid's 5th Postulate

They were parallel tracks for a while, the trains
running smoothly from depot to depot, carrying

the precious cargo. Then the terrain changed,
began to tilt, and my energy, pushing both engines

uphill, waxed and waned. After the cancer, I
canceled the schedule. Train spotting is a favorite

pastime for some people: the engineers wave
from up high like winning warriors, their faces

smeared with black soot; broad grins make their
teeth shine bright. It was another life. I was

the steam and the coal fire, the turning cogs and
the pumping pistons, the speed and the furious prod.

Today I only drive the engine of words, and it is
getting harder to watch neglected numbers jump

over tracks and barriers like wooly sheep and let
the whoosh of passing trains brush their coats.

Words fly uphill of their own will: I am the
breath, but not the driving force—not even that.

The other train is lost for good deep in the woods,
a sorry wreck abandoned where the tracks converged.

Forward to the Beginning

The difference between
a polyp and a tumor
is like the difference
between a polynomial
and a continuous function.

∞

How did I get from there to here
when all my relatives
gathering their brood around them
parted the tents' flaps
and looking up
toward the mountain top
saw Moses' face
beam down
from
above?

∞

Cottonmouth do not bite;
the apple was sour.

∞

I do not want to be a rib

∞

0

Doors

You spend your time pushing doors open,
running through doors
or toward doors in your future,
running through your future
unaware that doors opened in haste or
in excitement, on purpose or by chance,
opened for you by others as a gift, by fate,
as invitation to proceed
close one by one,
not with a bang but softly latching on
like time after a lag,
like time which slowly pours you
into your present image,
soft-shut on rooms you passed through
almost without notice,
large rooms, small rooms, wide rooms,
narrow rooms, square or oval rooms,
gigantic rooms whose edges disappear into
past's dust and memory.
All rooms become a corridor leading
towards one door
whose name you cannot say.

My Mother Speaks

My mother speaks beyond the ridge
where she resides since she has passed away
words of wisdom heard so long ago I thought forever lost.
I think she is still here although invisible—
she blends with the air and my thoughts.
She bends over my writing
as if trying to decipher a foreign word.
"Look here," she says, smiling serenely,
"no more mathematics—
you speak a language that is crystal clear."

Reflection About the *t*-Axis

A bag full of words.   A bag full of words.
Tomorrow—my favorite.   *Yesterday*—my favorite.
May I have it, please?   May I have it, please?

NOTES

P. 5, "Animals One to Seven." The Romanian word *melc* means *snail*. "Melc, melc, codobelc" is the first line of a Romanian children's song. Several animated versions of this song are available on YouTube.

P. 12, "Thirteen." 13 is my companion-number. I would like to believe it is my lucky number, the number following me like a shadow since the day of my birth on the 13th of August.

P. 16, "$\sqrt{2}$ = 1.41421. . . . ." In the 5th century BC, the Pythagorean Hippasus of Metapontum discovered the existence of irrational numbers. Particularly, he had shown that $\sqrt{2}$ — the length of the diagonal of a square with a unit side—is an irrational number. For his sin, legend has it, Hippasus was thrown overboard during a sea voyage. The poem plays with the imaginary possibility that his murder occurred before he breached the Pythagorean code of secrecy and made his discovery public. The line count of the poem's stanzas follows the decimal expansion of $\sqrt{2}$ to five decimal places.

P. 20, "The Death of Euclid." Euclid (323 BC–285 BC) lived in Alexandria, a Greek city situated in Egypt at the mouth of the Nile, and famous for its legendary library (housing 600,000 papyrus rolls), the Museum (a center of leaning rivaling Plato's Academy in Athens), and its lighthouse (an engineering marvel considered one of the Seven Wonders of the Ancient World). Euclid founded a school of mathematics at the Museum. Very little is known about his life beyond the monumental achievement of writing *The Elements*, a book that had profound impact on Western thought, and set the foundation for mathematical standards of reasoning for all time. Only the Bible has been more widely reprinted and studied.

P. 21, "13 January 2009." The poem's structure follows *The Fundamental Theorem of Arithmetic*, which states that every positive integer greater than 1 may be expressed in a unique way as a product of powers of distinct prime numbers. This technique was introduced by Carl Andre in his poem, "On the Sadness" (*Numerals 1924–1977*, Yale University Art Gallery Catalog Exhibit, 1978).

P. 26, "Calculus." The British mathematician and physicist Isaac Newton (1642–1727) and the German mathematician and philosopher Gottfried Leibniz (1646–1716) are considered to be the co-founders of Calculus. Their seminal achievement was the formulation and proof of *The Fun-*

damental Theorem of Calculus—a theorem that relates two disparate concepts: the concept of integration (used to calculate areas below a curve) and the concept of differentiation (employed to find formulas for tangent lines to curves). Although no one had made a successful connection between the two concepts before Newton and Leibniz, *The Fundamental Theorem of Calculus* has its roots in the work of numerous other mathematicians who studied each of these concepts separately for many years. In fact, the roots of this area of mathematics go back several thousand years to the invention of numerals by Hindu mathematicians.

P. 28, *"The Enigmatic Number e."* More detailed information about the historical figures and mathematical results mentioned in this poem may be found in the paper "The Enigmatic Number *e*: A History in Verse and its Uses in the Mathematics Classroom," by Sarah Glaz, *MAA Loci: Convergence*, April 10, 2010.

P. 31, "If Not Loved, Then Useful." *Mathematical Modeling in the Environment* by Charles Hadlock (MAA Press, 1998).

P. 37, "What Can We Do If We Crave Certainty in Mathematics?" Georg Cantor (1845–1918) is responsible for the rigorous mathematical representation of infinity and the development of set theory, the "language" that allowed mathematicians to work with the concept of infinity. Almost immediately after its discovery, a number of paradoxes were found in set theory, among them the famous *Barber Paradox*, posed by Bertrand Russell (1872–1970). Considerable efforts were made to fix these paradoxes, including the program proposed by the prominent German mathematician, David Hilbert (1862–1943), mentioned in the epigraph to this poem. These efforts were dealt a severe blow by the Incompleteness Theorems proved by Kurt Gödel (1906–1978). Fortunately, it was not the end of the road. Realizing the exact extent of uncertainty inherent in the mathematical system had the beneficial effect of removing vague anxieties and redirecting research focus.

P. 39, "Hardy." G. H. Hardy (1877–1947) was a British mathematician who made significant contributions to Number Theory. His mathematical powers declined when, at the age of 62, he suffered a heart attack. Shortly after, he wrote *A Mathematician's Apology*, a book of haunting beauty and sadness, which inspired many towards mathematics.

P. 45, "Commutative Coherent Rings." *Commutative Coherent Rings* by

Sarah Glaz, Lecture Notes in Mathematics 137, Springer-Verlag, 1989. Reissued by Springer Online and Print-on-Demand, 2007.

P. 51, "Not Human." The poem is a response to a television interview with Daniel Tammet, author of *Thinking in Numbers* (Little Brown and Co., 2012), and possessor of an extraordinary brain.

P. 62, "Late Afternoon at the Workshop on Commutative Rings." The mathematical result referred to in this poem is the solution to Kaplansky's Conjecture, a conjecture posed by prominent algebraist Irving Kaplansky (1917–2006) in 1965, whose final solution was announced by Thomas Lucas in 2006 at the conference in Cortona, Italy. Lucas' solution was the culmination of work carried out by a number of algebraists and built on ideas of previous partial solutions by Hwa Tsang (1965), Wolmer Vasconcelos and Sarah Glaz (1998), and Alan Loper and Moshe Roitman (2005). More details on the work concerning this conjecture, and the area of study generated by its solution, may be found in the paper "Prüfer Conditions in Commutative Rings" by Sarah Glaz and Ryan Schwarz, *Arabian Journal for Science and Engineering* 36, 967-983, 2011.

P. 71, "Luminy Light." The golden ratio or divine proportion, denoted by ϕ, is the number $(1 + \sqrt{5})/2 = 1.6180339...$. ϕ is an ancient number which appears in sources as old as Euclid's *Elements*. Of more recent vintage (and controversially so) ϕ is believed to be an ancient aesthetic principle whose appearance in a visual object renders the object most pleasing to the viewer.

P. 75, "On the Way to New Jersey in Winter of 2000." This is a Fibonacci poem: the syllable count of the poem's stanzas follows the Fibonacci sequence— the infinite sequence of numbers beginning with 0, 1, 1, 2, 3, 5, 8, 13, ... in which each number is the sum of the two previous numbers. The poem ends at Fibonacci number 144.

P. 92, "Reflection About the *t*-Axis." Mathematics considers time, denoted by t, to be the fourth dimension of physical reality. If this could have been visually depicted in our three-dimensional space, it would have involved a fourth axis, the *t*-axis. "Reflection about a line" is a mathematical phrase describing the symmetry achieved by flipping an image across a line.

ACKNOWLEDGEMENTS

I thank the editors of the following publications, in which some of the poems in this book first appeared, sometimes in previous incarnations:

"Do You Believe in Fairytales?" in the paper "Mathematical Pattern Poetry," by Sarah Glaz, *Proceedings of Bridges Towson*, 2012

"Love Story" and "Late Afternoon at the Workshop on Commutative Rings," in the anthology *Strange Attractors: Poems of Love and Mathematics*, AK Peters, 2008

"Pythagoras Plays His Lyre," *Journal of Humanistic Mathematics*, 2016

"13 January 2009," *Recursive Angel*, 2011

"I Am a Number," *Journal of Humanistic Mathematics*, 2011

"I Am a Number II," *Talking Writing*, 2012

"Calculus," *Humanistic Mathematics Network Journal*, 2002

"The Enigmatic Number *e*," in the paper "The Enigmatic Number *e*: A History in Verse and its Uses in the Mathematics Classroom," by Sarah Glaz, *MAA Loci: Convergence*, 2010

"Eclipse, a Love Poem," in the anthology *Bridges 2016 Poetry Anthology*, Tessellations Publishing, 2016

"Mathematical Modeling," *London Grip*, 2013

"A Pantoum for the Power of Theorems," in the blog *Intersections— Poetry with Mathematics*, 2013

"The Integers Are Not a Happy Medium" and "Forward to the Beginning," *Talking Writing*, 2016

"Ghazal: Resonant Air," *The Ghazal Page*, 2010

"Departures in May," *Ibis Review*, 1995

"Reflection About the *t*-Axis," in the paper "Poems Structured by Integer Sequences," by Sarah Glaz, *Journal of Mathematics and the Arts*, 2016

$\sqrt{2}$ = 1.41421...," "The First Negative," "Numbers and Letters," "The Death of Euclid," "Calculus," "What Can We Do If We Crave Certainty in Mathematics?," and "Hardy," will appear as a "poetry folder" in *Journal of Humanistic Mathematics*, 2018.

In addition, I am grateful for the inspiring visual poem "Sun Plus Moon" by Karl Kempton; the amazing photographs of Venice by Ron Glaz and in particular, "Window to Venice," which hangs on the wall of my study and brings me joy every time I look at it; and the anonymous mathematical artist who crafted the mandala necklace I bought on a street corner in Lisbon. Thanks are also due to the Yale University Art Gallery for permission to use Kandinsky's "Small Yellow" as a cover image, to Shannon McAvoy for the author photo, to Claudine Burns-Smith for the photographs of the mandala necklace and of "Window to Venice," to Craig Kaplan for the diagrams on the chapters' title pages, and to Robert Fathauer for help with typesetting equations. My special thanks go to Antrim House publisher, the fine poet Rennie McQuilkin, for the extraordinary work and care he put into the preparation of this manuscript and the beautiful design of the finished book.

This collection would not exist without encouragement and support from friends and family. In particular, I thank Claudine Burns-Smith, Vera Schwarcz, Riva Berleant and Marc Rubenstein for many years of friendship, lively conversations on art, books, poetry and mathematics, and generous help and advice when needed. I also thank my newer friends, the growing community of Bridges poets, for comradeship and inspiration. Last, but not least, I thank my husband, Joe Glaz, and our son, Ron Glaz; their presence in my life makes everything possible.

OTHER WORKS BY THE AUTHOR

POETRY VOLUMES

Sarah Glaz (editor), *Bridges 2016 Poetry Anthology*, Tessellations Publishing, 2016

Sarah Glaz (guest editor), *Journal of Mathematics and the Arts, Special Issue: Poetry and Mathematics,* Taylor & Francis / CRC Press, Vol. 8, Issues 1-2, 2014

Sarah Glaz (editor), *Bridges 2013 Poetry Anthology,* Tessellations Publishing, 2013

Sarah Glaz & JoAnne Growncy (editors), *Strange Attractors: Poems of Love and Mathematics,* CRC Press / AK Peters, 2008

POETRY VIDEO

Sarah Glaz (coordinator), Mike Naylor (host), Steve Stamps (movie editor), *Bridges 2014 Virtual Anthology: The Mathematical Poetry Reading at Bridges Seoul,* Bridges Organization, 2014 (https://www.youtube.com/watch?v=fcaL2PXuy7U&feature=youtu.be)

MATHEMATICS VOLUMES

Marco Fontana, Sophie Frisch, Sarah Glaz, Francesca Tartarone & Paolo Zanardo (editors), *Rings, Polynomials, and Modules*, Springer, 2017

Marco Fontana, Sophie Frisch & Sarah Glaz (editors), *Commutative Algebra: Recent Advances in Commutative Rings, Integer-valued Polynomials and Polynomial Functions*, Springer, 2014

James Brewer, Sarah Glaz, William Heinzer & Bruce Olberding (editors), *Multiplicative Ideal Theory in Commutative Algebra: a Tribute to the Work of Robert Gilmer,* Springer, 2006

Scott Chapman & Sarah Glaz (editors), *Non-Noetherian Commutative Ring Theory*, Springer / Kluwer Academic Publishers, MAIA 520, 2000

Sarah Glaz, *Commutative Coherent Rings*, Springer Verlag Lecture Notes in Math. 1371, 1989. Reissued by Springer Online and Print-on-Demand, 2007

PAPERS

A complete list of publications and the preprints of papers written after 2000 on both mathematics and the connections between mathematics and poetry are available from the author's website: http://www.math. uconn.edu/~glaz.

ABOUT THE AUTHOR

Sarah Glaz has moved from culture to culture and from language to language several times in her life. Born in Bucharest, Romania, she emigrated with her parents to Israel at age 11. After completing a Bachelor Degree in mathematics and philosophy at Tel Aviv University, she and her husband came to the United States as graduate students at Rutgers University. This was the site of two major events in Sarah's life: her son was born shortly after she passed the prelims, and she was introduced to Commutative Ring Theory and completed a Ph.D. thesis in this area of mathematics. Sarah went on to a research and teaching career in mathematics, joining the faculty of the Mathematics Department at the University of Connecticut in 1989. By the time of her retirement in 2017, Sarah had authored or edited about ninety publications and received several grants and prestigious visiting positions. In 2007 she was elected a University Teaching Fellow.

Sarah has written poetry in the languages of all the countries where she has lived: Romanian, Hebrew and English. She is not far from poetry even in the country of mathematics, where her area of research falls into the region of pure mathematics, which according to Einstein is "the poetry of logical ideas." Sarah started writing poetry in English in 1991 and found, to her delight, that the mathematics which shaped her life found its way into her poetry. Since then, her poetry and translations from various languages have appeared in a number of literary and mathematical journals and in several anthologies. This is Sarah's first poetry collection.

Sarah serves as Associate Editor for the *Journal of Mathematics and the Arts:* http://www.tandfonline.com/toc/tmaa20/current. She is also the organizer of mathematical poetry readings at the annual Bridges conferences: http://www.math.uconn.edu/~glaz/Mathematical_Poetry_at_Bridges/index.html.

For more information about Sarah's publications and activities, visit her website: http://www.math.uconn.edu/~glaz.

This book is set in Garamond Premier Pro, which originated in 1988 when type-designer Robert Slimbach visited the Plantin-Moretus Museum in Antwerp, Belgium, to study its collection of Claude Garamond's metal punches and typefaces. During the mid-fifteen hundreds, Garamond—a Parisian punch-cutter—produced a refined array of book types that combined an unprecedented degree of balance and elegance, for centuries standing as the pinnacle of beauty and practicality in type-founding. Slimbach has created an entirely new interpretation based on Garamond's designs and on compatible italics cut by Robert Granjon, Garamond's contemporary.

To order additional copies of this book
or other Antrim House titles, contact the publisher at

Antrim House
21 Goodrich Rd., Simsbury, CT 06070
860.217.0023, AntrimHouse@comcast.net
or the house website (www.AntrimHouseBooks.com).

•

On the house website
in addition to information on books
you will find sample poems, upcoming events,
and a "seminar room" featuring supplemental biography,
notes, images, poems, reviews, and
writing suggestions.